Black, Brown, Beautiful Hair

Coloring and Activity Book for African American Girls Encouraging Self Love

By: S.L. Denise

Disclaimer

While the author has taken utmost efforts to ensure the accuracy of the written content, all readers are advised to follow information mentioned herein at their own risk. The author cannot be held responsible for any personal or commercial damage caused by misinterpretation of information. All readers are encouraged to seek professional advice when needed.

This book has been written for information purposes only. Every effort has been made to make this book as complete and accurate as possible. However, there may be mistakes in typography or content. Also, this book provides information only up to the publishing date. Therefore, it should be used as a guide - not as the ultimate source.

The purpose of this book is to educate. The author and the publisher do not warrant that the information contained in this book is fully complete and shall not be responsible for any errors or omissions. The author and publisher shall have neither liability nor responsibility to any person or entity with respect to any loss or damage caused or alleged to be caused directly or indirectly by this book.

HEY THERE!
THANK YOU FOR PURCHASING THIS COLORING AND ACTIVITY BOOK. I HOPE YOU ENJOY EVERY PART OF IT. THIS PROJECT WAS TRULY MADE WITH LOVE.
IF YOU ENJOYED THIS BOOK, PLEASE DO NOT FORGET TO LEAVE A REVIEW ON AMAZON OR THE OUTLET YOU PURCHASE FROM. A SIMPLE REVIEW HELPS US OUT A LOT. THANK YOU!

My Profile Page

My favorite color is :

My favorite food is :

My favorite game is :

My best friend is :

My favorite cartoon is :

My favorite season is :

My favorite holiday is :

My favorite book is :

My favorite feature is :

My best talent is :

SWATCH YOUR COLORS

Red

Blue

Green

Yellow

Pink

Purple

Orange

Gray

Brown

White

Black

HELP COURTNEY GET TO DANCE CLASS

I Am

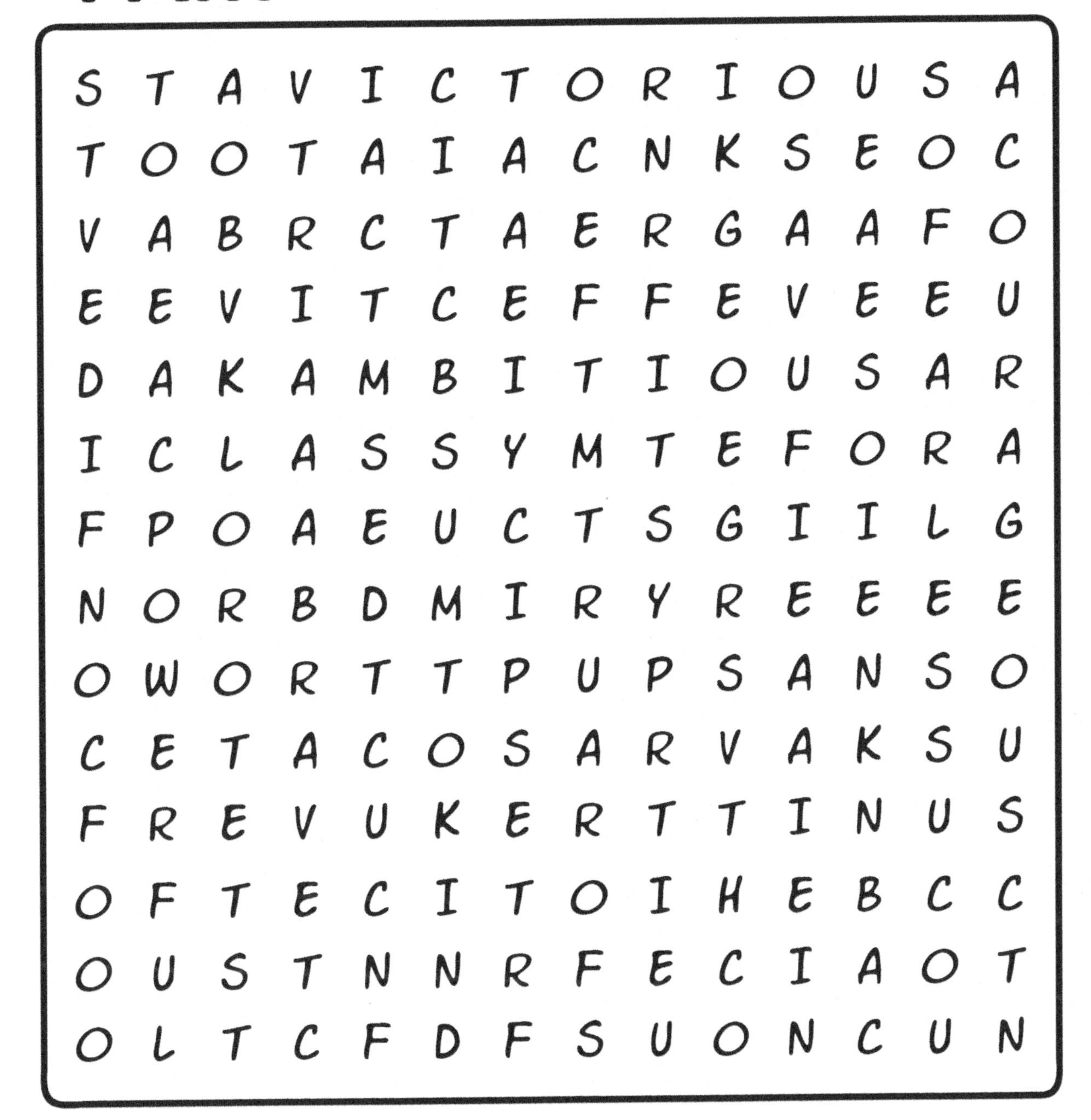

Find each word listed below in the cross word table.
Take your time and have fun

AMBITIOUS
BRAVE
CLASSY
CONFIDENT
COURAGEOUS
EFFECTIVE
EMPATHETIC
GREAT
FEARLESS
KIND
POWERFUL
VICTORIOUS

Tic Tac Toe

Instructions: Get 3 in a row to win

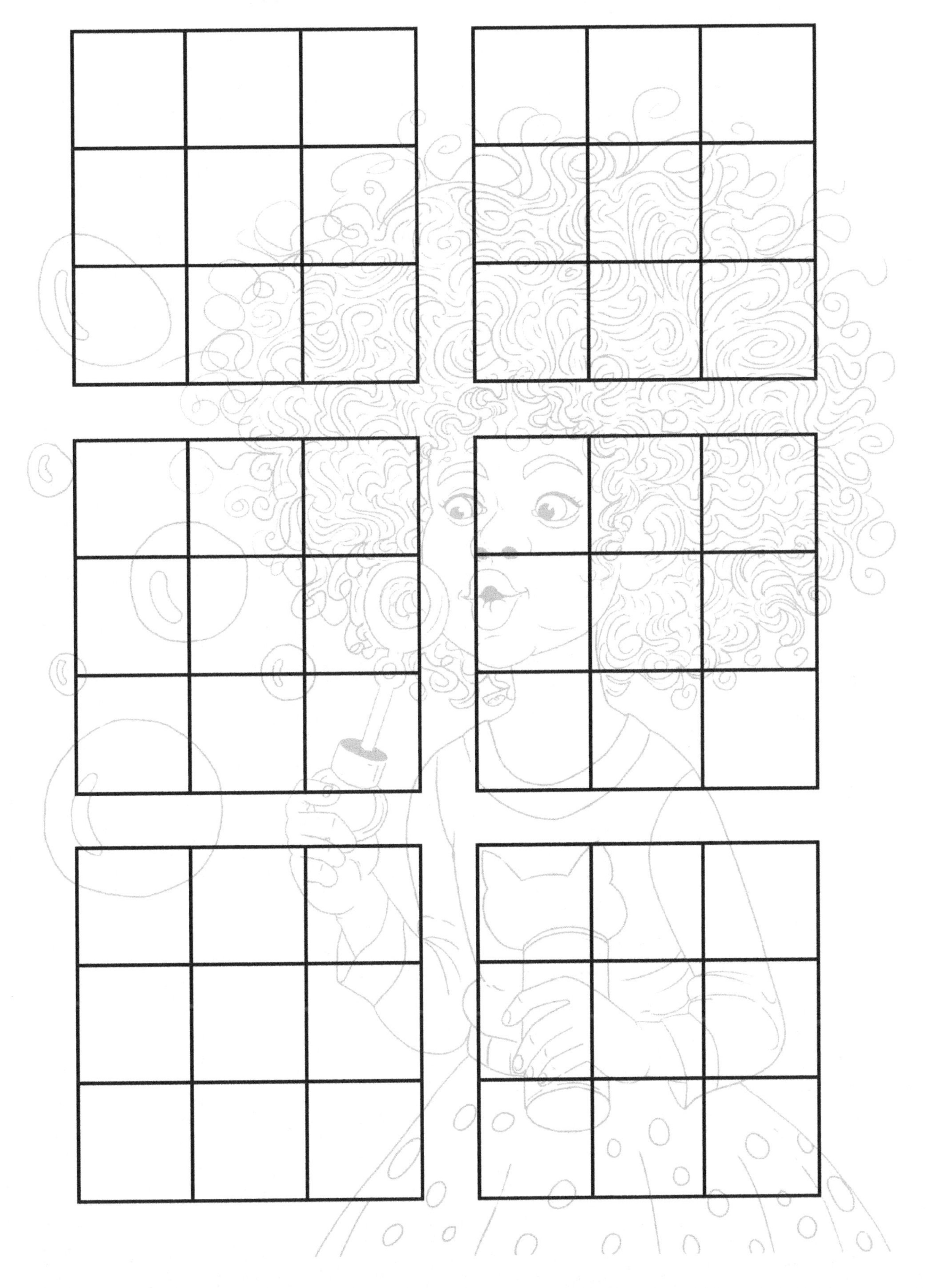

I Am

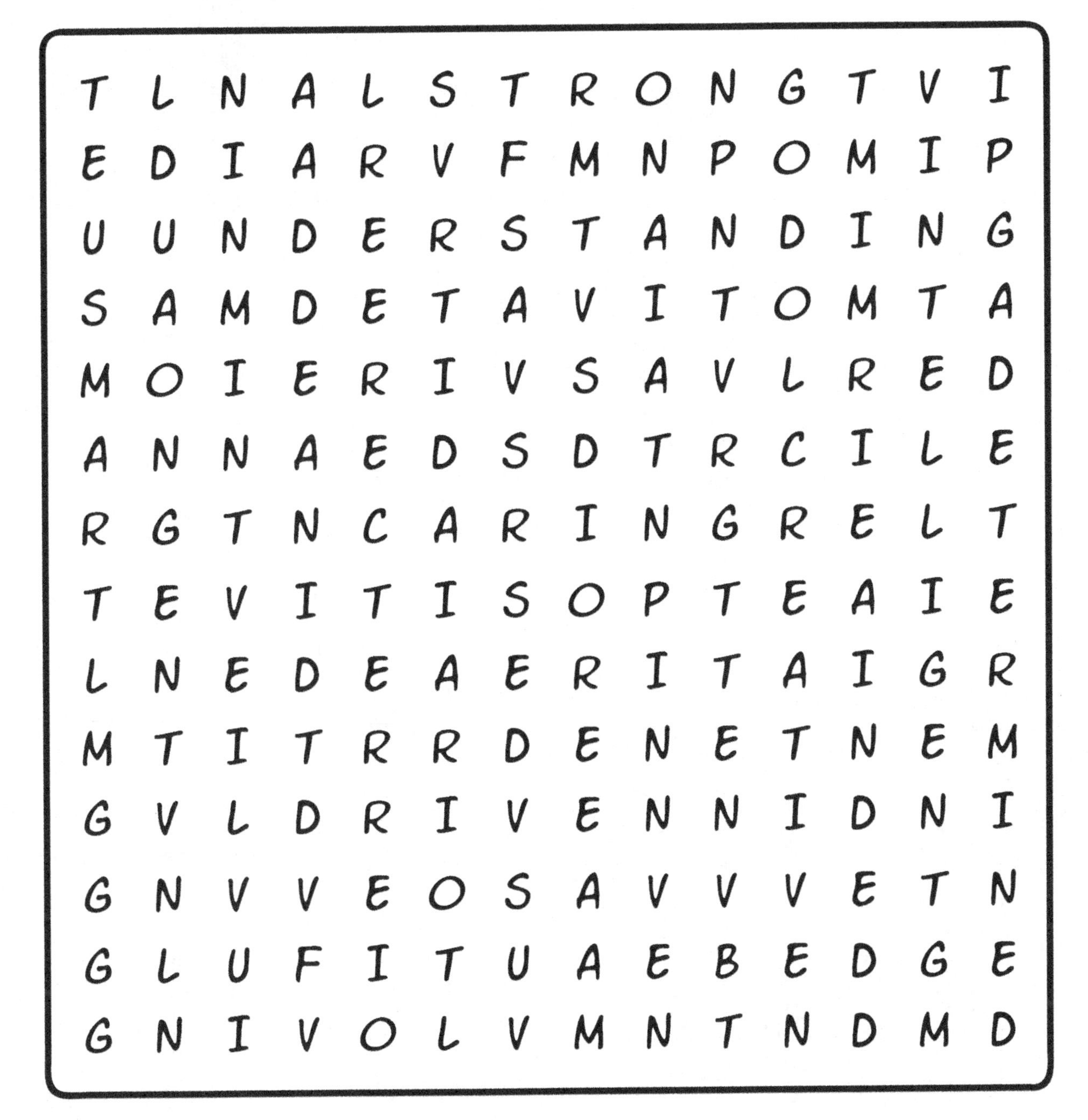

Find each word listed below in the cross word table.
Take your time and have fun

BEAUTIFUL	DRIVEN	POSITIVE
CARING	INTELLIGENT	SMART
CREATIVE	LOVING	STRONG
DETERMINED	MOTIVATED	UNDERSTANDING

Tic Tac Toe

Instructions: Get 3 in a row to win

HAIR WORD SCRAMBLE

Decode the scrambled word to see what you find. Find the keyword box at the bottom right of the page.

latiyopn ____________________

snbu ____________________

wssti ____________________

eavws ____________________

roaf ____________________

yrluc ____________________

slico ____________________

eretarbt ____________________

Keyword Box

Afro	Waves
Curly	Twists
Barrette	Coils
Buns	Ponytails

GUIDE DOROTHY TO SCHOOL

POSITIVE WORDS SCRAMBLE

Decode the scrambled word to see what you find. Find the keyword box at the bottom right of the page.

sourneeg ____________________

antgeel ____________________

eflagrcu ____________________

disope ____________________

riabeel ____________________

erusce ____________________

futrhutl ____________________

tanbrvi ____________________

Keyword Box

Elegant	Generous
Reliable	Poised
Secure	Vibrant
Graceful	Truthful

Tic Tac Toe

Instructions: Get 3 in a row to win

COLORS WORD SCRAMBLE

Decode the scrambled word to see what you find. Find the keyword box at the bottom right of the page.

elprpu ______________________

eulb ______________________

yanomag ______________________

oisetqusur ______________________

gernao ______________________

owbnr ______________________

weylol ______________________

atn ______________________

Keyword Box

Purple	Yellow
Blue	Orange
Brown	Turquoise
Mahogany	Tan

My Future Is Bright

O	E	E	R	E	L	A	W	Y	E	R	N	R	G
R	M	A	E	R	D	S	Y	A	U	E	E	E	I
T	E	R	A	D	M	I	Y	N	C	N	U	G	R
S	C	I	E	N	T	I	S	T	E	G	E	S	R
D	I	L	L	S	R	E	L	N	D	I	G	E	E
N	G	I	O	E	S	E	S	I	T	N	D	N	G
P	R	E	S	I	D	E	N	T	U	E	E	N	R
T	C	S	E	E	I	E	C	R	N	E	S	E	U
M	E	E	E	A	T	R	S	C	A	R	N	W	W
C	O	L	L	E	G	E	E	I	U	I	N	I	W
C	D	O	I	R	T	R	U	S	I	S	S	N	G
G	E	N	T	R	E	P	R	E	N	E	U	R	N
N	U	C	E	D	U	C	A	T	O	R	S	G	N
U	S	A	N	Y	N	D	L	R	O	T	C	O	D

Find each word listed below in the cross word table.
Take your time and have fun

COLLEGE
DOCTOR
DREAM
EDUCATOR
ENGINEER
ENTREPRENEUR
LAWYER
NURSE
PRESIDENT
SCIENTIST
SUCCESS
WIN

Tic Tac Toe

Instructions: Get 3 in a row to win

GUIDE MYA TO THE LIBRARY

Hair Care

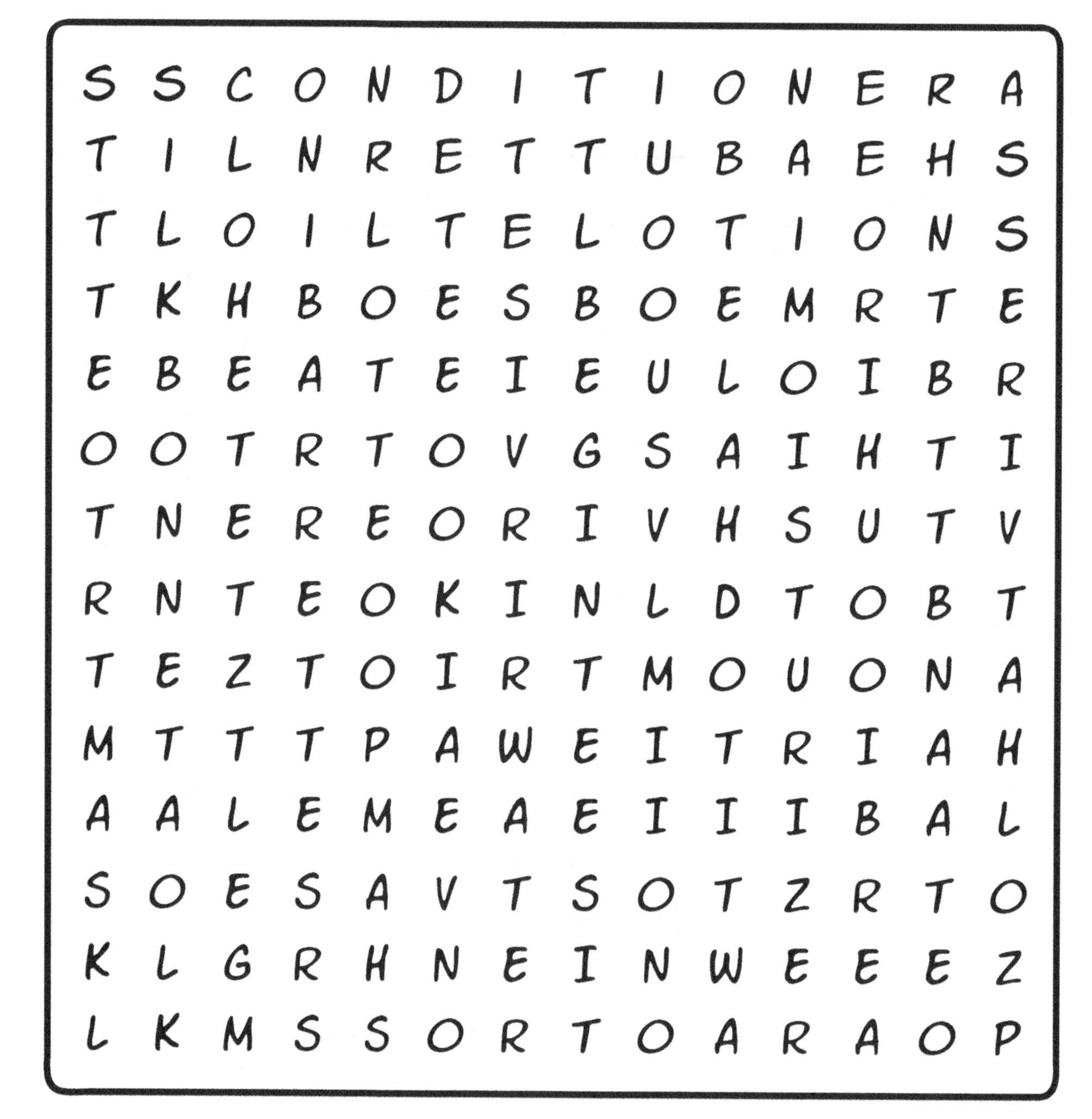

Find each word listed below in the cross word table.
Take your time and have fun

BARRETTE	LOTION	SHAMPOO
CONDITIONER	MASK	SHEA BUTTER
GEL	MOISTURIZER	SILK BONNET
HAIR TIE	OLIVE OIL	WATER

Tic Tac Toe

Instructions: Get 3 in a row to win

HELP MANAE GET TO THE PARK

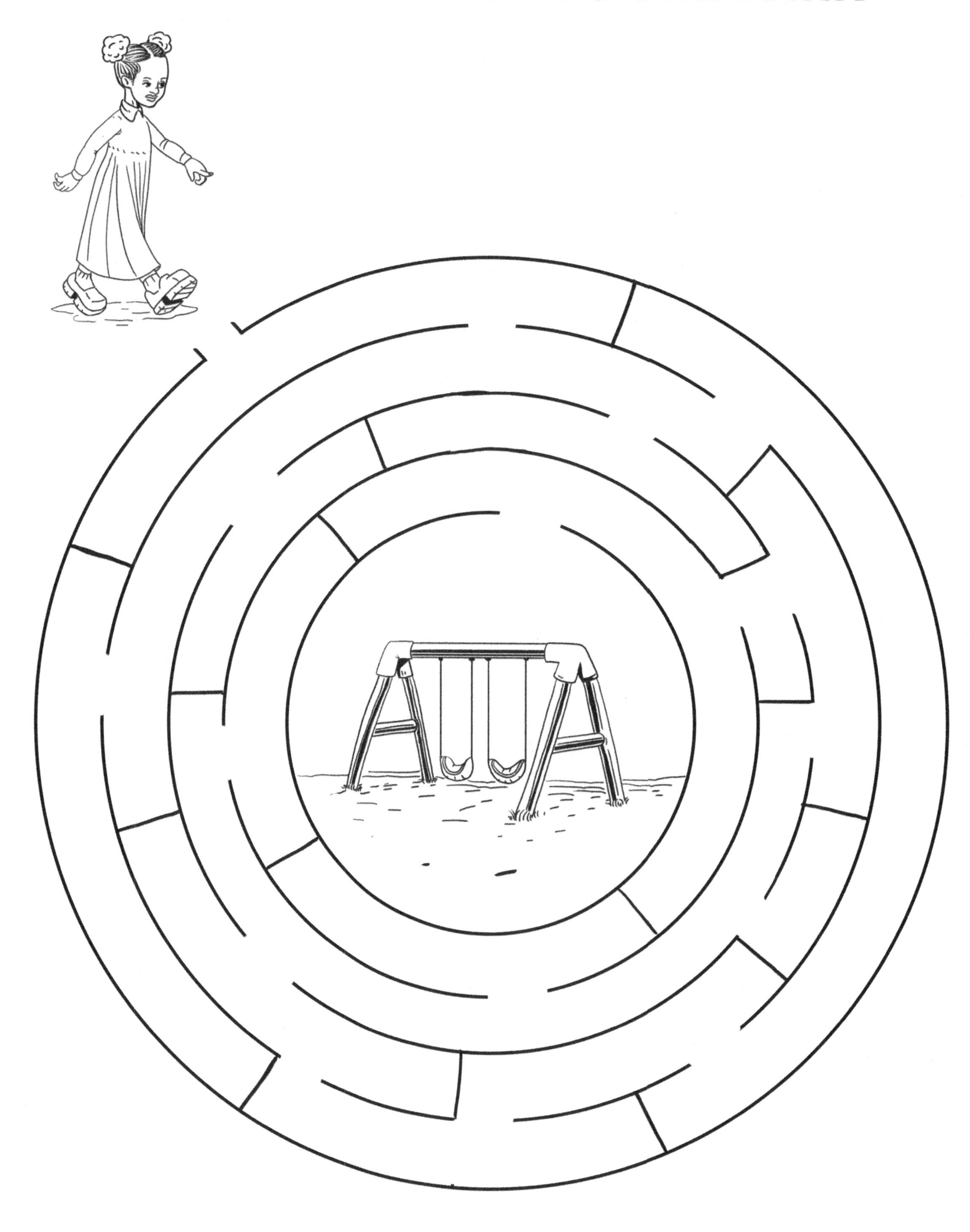

My Hair Is Unique

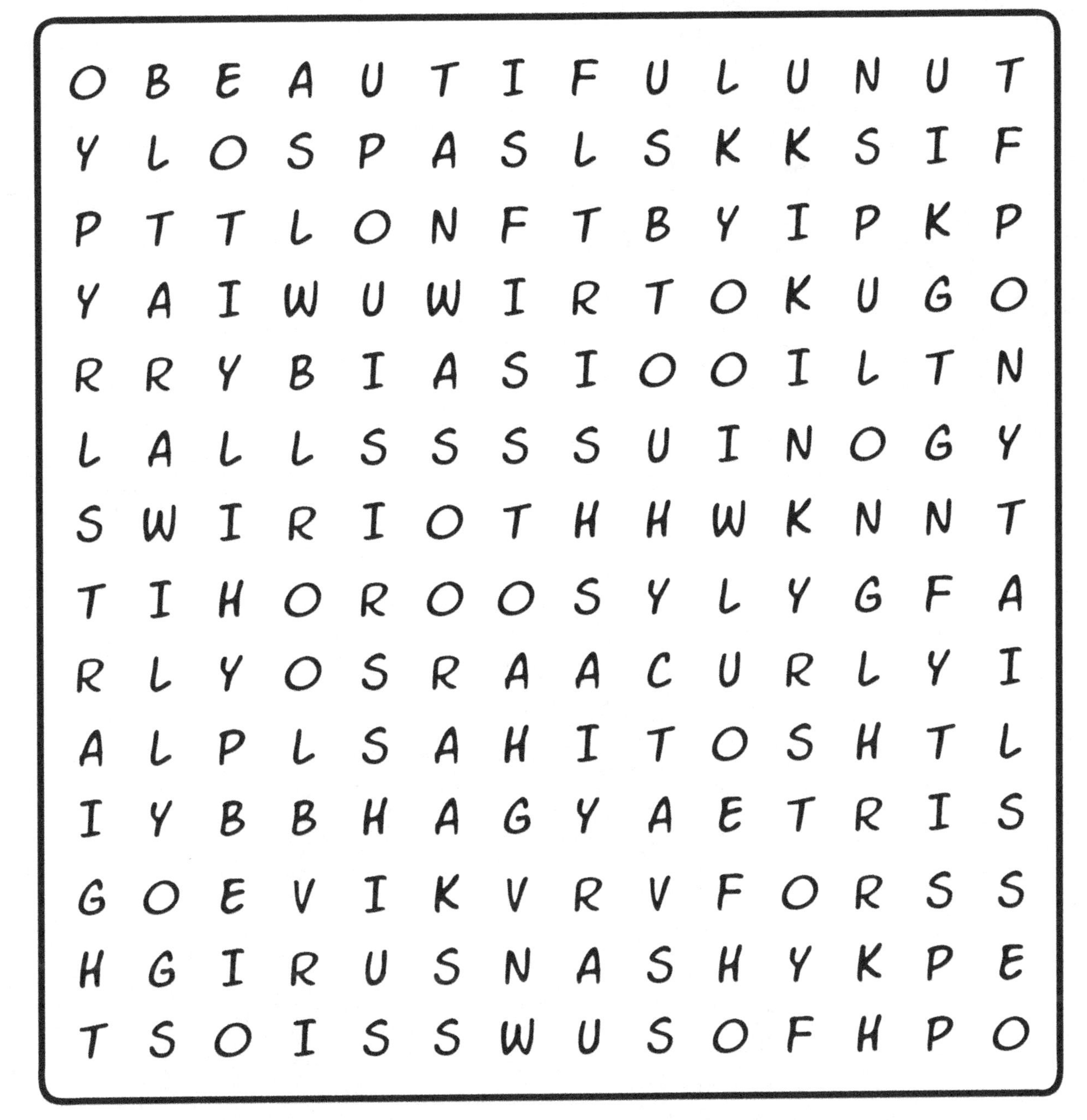

Find each word listed below in the cross word table.
Take your time and have fun

AFRO
BEAUTIFUL
BUNS
CURLY
KINKY
LONG
PONYTAILS
POROSITY
SHORT
STRAIGHT
TWISTS
WAVES

I Love My

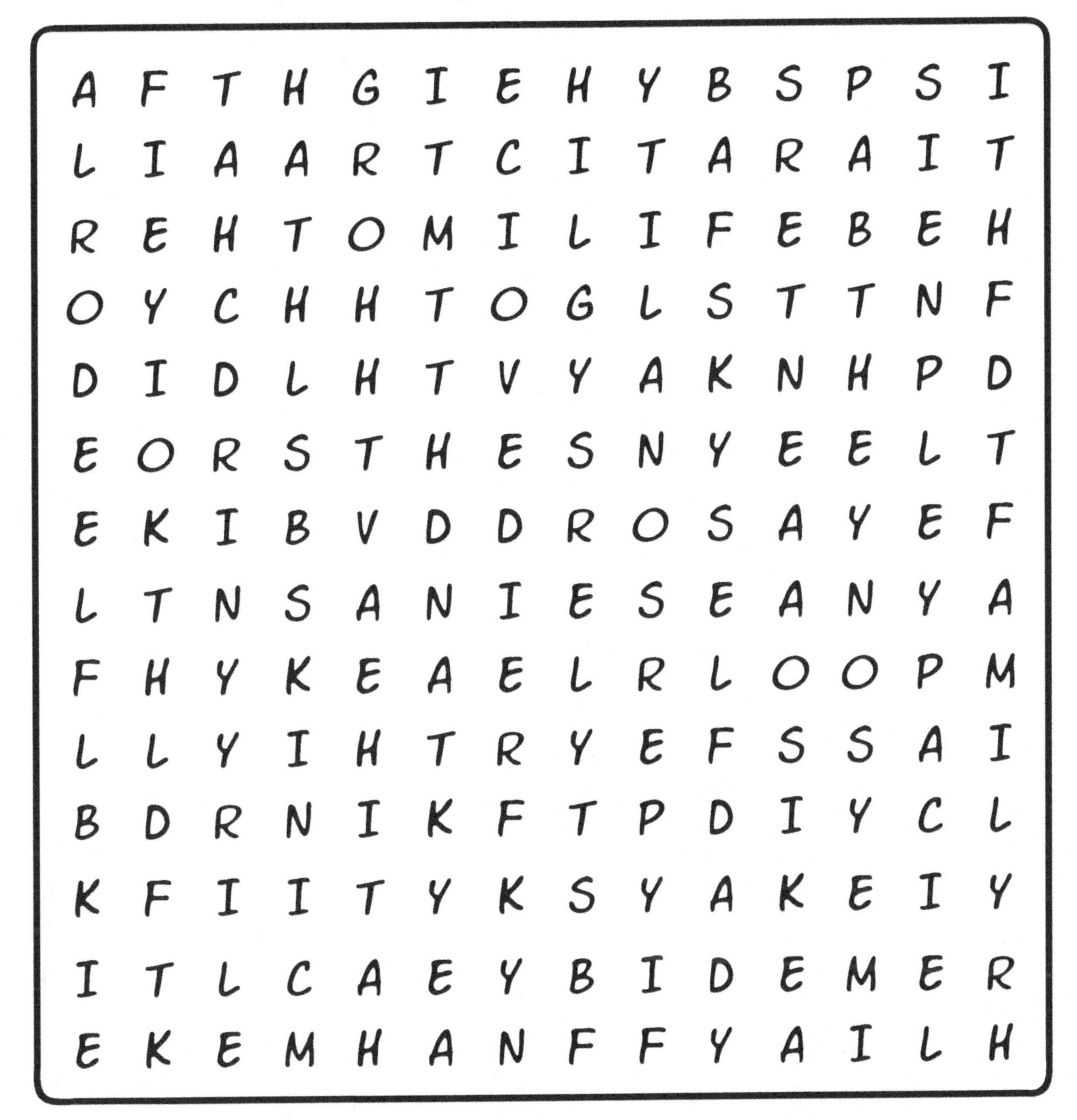

Find each word listed below in the cross word table.
Take your time and have fun

BIKE
DAD
FAMILY
FRIENDS

HAIR
HEIGHT
MOTHER
SELF

SKIN
STYLE
PERSONALITY
VOICE

RIDE WITH SARAH TO THE AMUSEMENT PARK

COLORS WORD SCRAMBLE

Decode the scrambled word to see what you find. Find the keyword box at the bottom right of the page.

tevoil ______________________

knip ______________________

nuruba ______________________

oignid ______________________

clabk ______________________

etwhi ______________________

echap ______________________

nereg ______________________

Keyword Box

Auburn	Green
Pink	Violet
Black	Indigo
Peach	White

FAMILY WORD SCRAMBLE

Unscramble the words and draw a picture of each family member.
Find the keyword box at the bottom of the page.

ytnua

____

pandrag

____

ecein

____

oucsin

____

elunc

____

glisbin

____

Sibling Niece Aunty Grandpa Uncle

Tic Tac Toe

Instructions: Get 3 in a row to win

FAMILY WORD SCRAMBLE

Unscramble the worvds and draw a picture of each family member.
Find the keyword box at the bottom of the page.

rohmte	drmagna	idclh
________	________	________
tsesri	arhfte	hrborte
________	________	________

Mother Father Grandma Brother Sister

HELP MOM GET TO THE GROCERY STORE

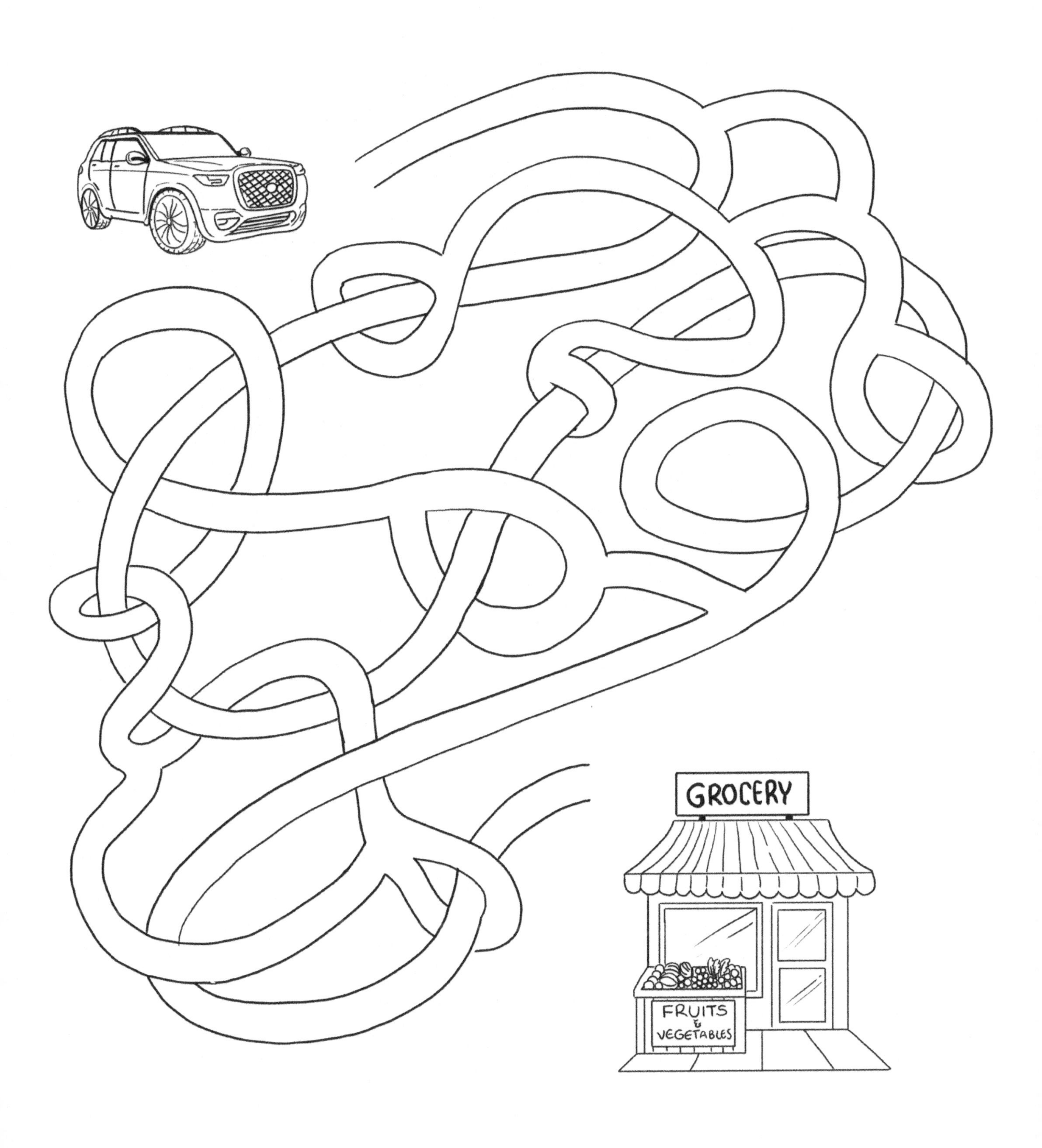

HEY THERE!
THANK YOU FOR PURCHASING THIS COLORING AND ACTIVITY BOOK. I HOPE YOU ENJOY EVERY PART OF IT. THIS PROJECT WAS TRULY MADE WITH LOVE.
IF YOU ENJOYED THIS BOOK, PLEASE DO NOT FORGET TO LEAVE A REVIEW ON AMAZON OR THE OUTLET YOU PURCHASE FROM. A SIMPLE REVIEW HELPS US OUT A LOT. THANK YOU!

Made in the USA
Monee, IL
03 December 2021